D0655564

A GOLDEN BOOK®

Western Publishing Company Inc, Racine, Wisconsin 53404.

Copyright © 1994 Brainwaves Limited. All rights reserved. Printed in Singapore,
unauthorised reproduction prohibited.

GOLDEN® , GOLDEN & DESIGN® , A GOLDEN BOOK® , and A LITTLE GOLDEN BOOK®
are registered trademarks of Western Publishing Company Inc. Published in the U.K.
by Western Publishing Company Inc., 25-31 Tavistock Place, London WC1H 9SU.

Oceans

Written by Keith Faulkner
Illustrated by Paul Johnson

Beneath the ocean he lies deep.
Though he is still, he's not asleep.

He sees each creature passing by.
Nothing escapes his giant eye.

But he himself is rarely seen.
He changes colour to match the scene.

You can't escape this monster's charms,
Or the octopus's suckered arms.

Just like a dinosaur, but smaller.
On rocks you'll find this seaside crawler.

Silently this reptile stands,
On the far-off Galapagos Islands.

Seaweed is what it loves to eat,
And basking in the tropical heat.

The world it has no stranger fauna,
Than the crested marine iguana.

Around the coast of the land down under,
You'll find a fish that is a wonder.

Swimming around the ocean bed.
Just like a carpet with a head.

With patterning and tasselled skin
You can't see where this fish begins.

Say carpet shark and you won't be wrong,
But its other name is the wobbegong.

Please don't laugh at this little chap.
He's well protected from mishap.

He lives with the anemone,
Who'd sting the likes of you and me.

No stinging tentacles he feels,
As he finishes his guardian's meals.

While other fish die from the sting,
The clown fish doesn't feel a thing.

Off Australia's north east coast
Lies a natural wonder of which they boast.

They call it the Great Barrier Reef,
So big it's quite beyond belief.

But something small is eating it.
Destroying the great reef bit by bit.

What loves to eat this coral dish?
It's name - the crown-of-thorns starfish.

In a crevice, hidden away,
There hides a creature, brownish grey.

Just like an underwater snake,
It lies in wait, it's prey to take.

Then out it strikes to grab it's prey,
And very few things get away.

The last things these poor creatures feel,
Are the fearsome teeth of the moray eel.

This small crustacean has one great lack.
There's no hard shell on it's soft back.

So it finds one lying on the sea bed,
And uses that as a home instead.

Then as it grows and the shell gets tight,
It finds another that fits just right.

So when you find a shell, take care.
A hermit crab may live in there.

This creature is a mammal and,
It lives in water, not on land.

With shining skin of black and white,
This hunter is an awesome sight.

They prowl beneath the frozen seas
And catch the swimming seals with ease.

Beneath the howling arctic gale,
Are the hunting grounds of the killer whale.